NESSIE'S SECRET

written by Susan Cohen

illustrated by Oumaima El Gamraoui

SUSAN COHEN

Beneath gentle waves
In the watery blue
Nessie has a secret
To share with you

She's lived in Loch Ness
For years upon years
Where folk search for her
With wonder and fear

They look high and low
Yet they never sneak
A peek at the monster
That they all seek

For all of this time
She's kept everyone guessing
Who is she? What is she?
Is there something they're missing?

What does she look like?
What does she eat?
Does she have flippers?
Or giant webbed feet?

NESSIE'S SECRET

7

Maybe she swims?
Maybe she walks?
Maybe she sings?
Maybe she talks?

Is she real?
Is she dreamed up?
Is that her true image
On those souvenir cups?

NESSIE'S SECRET

11

So many questions
About one special being
Who's quietly content
Without anyone seeing

She knows who she is
She feels perfect peace
Tranquil and calm
No stress to release

For that is her secret
As simple as that
No need for fanfare
Or big party hats

Nessie's content
In the skin that she's wearing
She's unique, she is special
No need for comparing

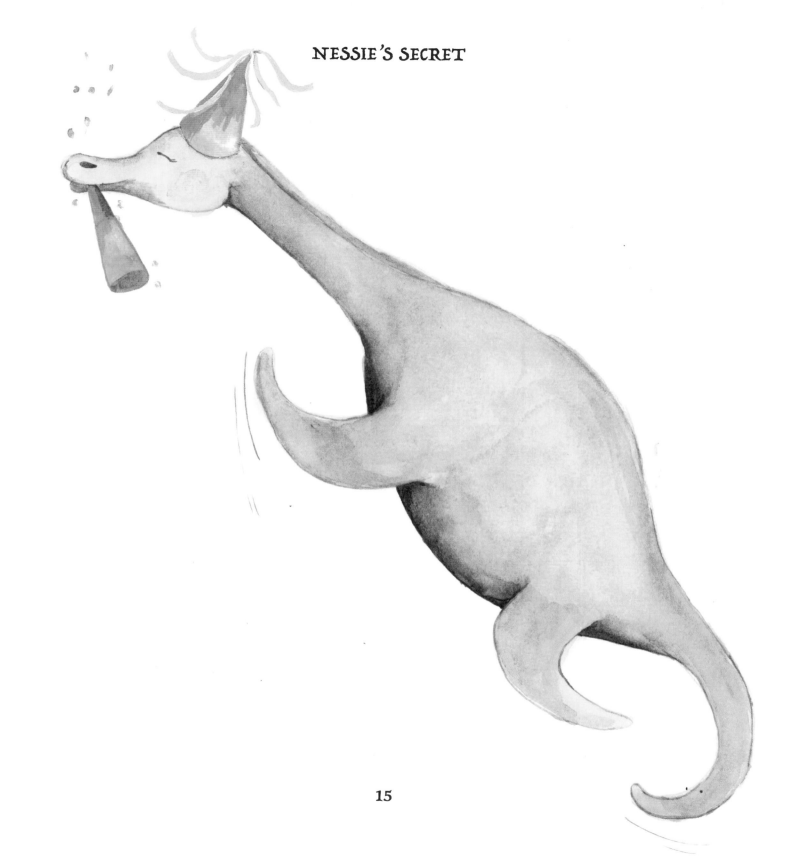

To dinosaurs, fish
Serpents or seals
Nessie's secret
Is to her own self, she's real

SUSAN COHEN

She loves to dive down
To the loch's deep dark lairs
With their green growing plants
Bubbling clear Highland air

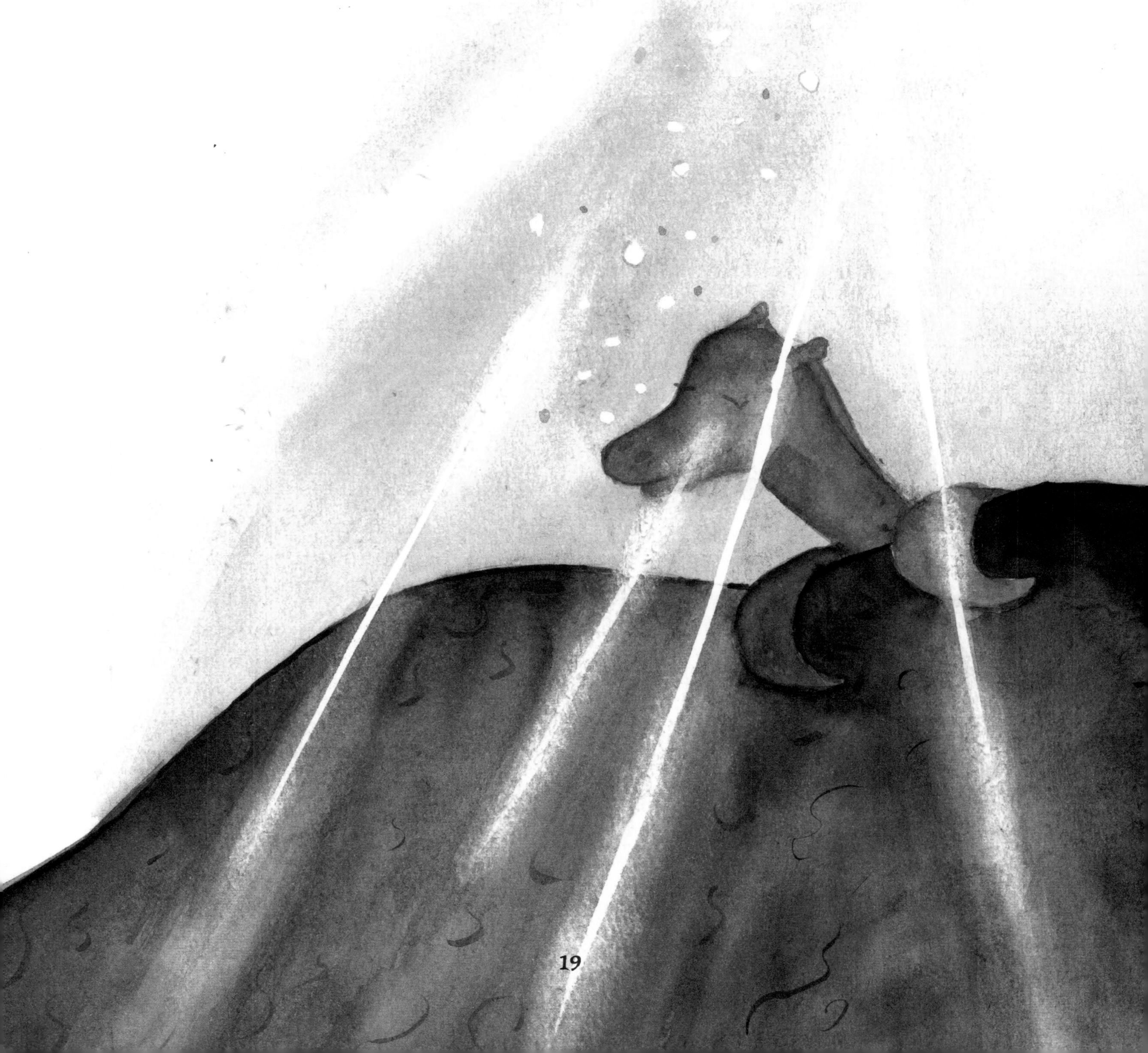

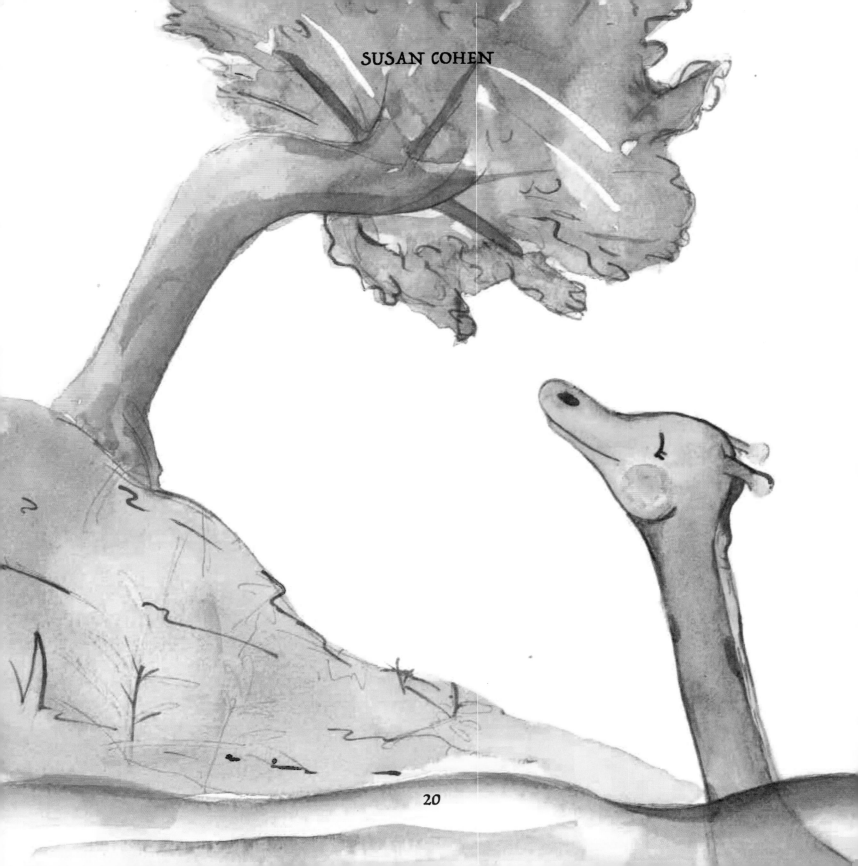

SUSAN COHEN

20

She loves to surface
And feel the warm breeze
As she watches the herons
And leaves on the trees

She feels wild and free
Living life her own way
Swimming brimming with joy
Loving every day

The loch is her home
Her own special place
A hideaway that
Brings a smile to her face

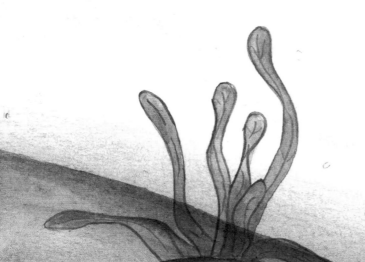

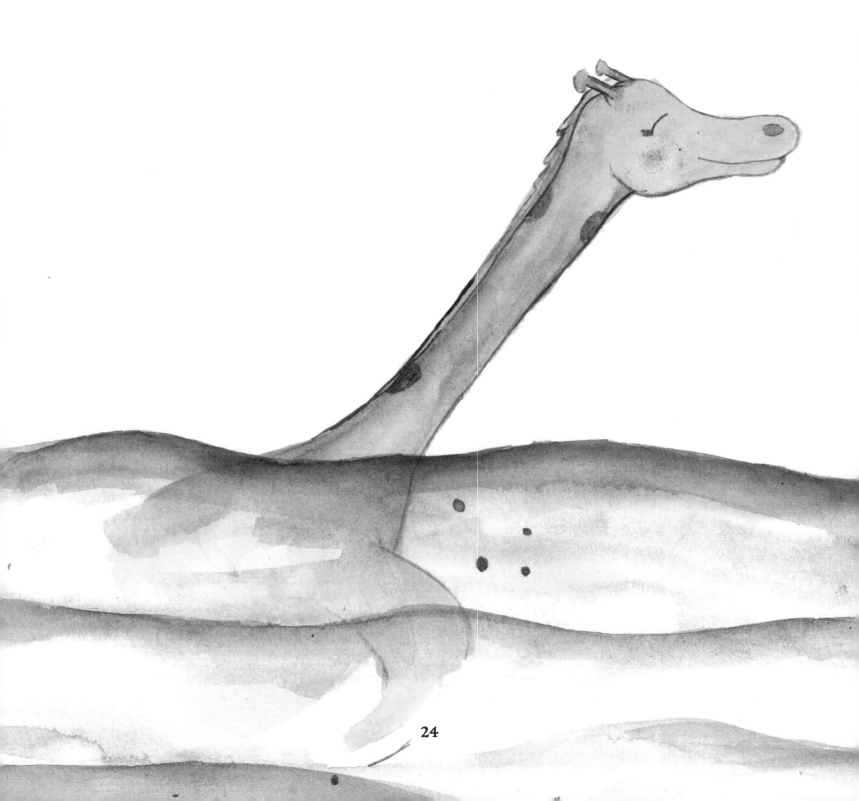

24

She is her own mystery
And you are too
You are unique
You are special YOU!

You're one of a kind
There's no-one like you
So stand tall and proud
So much you can do!

Your life's more than being
Your life is for living
No matter what hoots
That others are giving

So find your own joys
Whatever they are
For in your own life
You are the star!

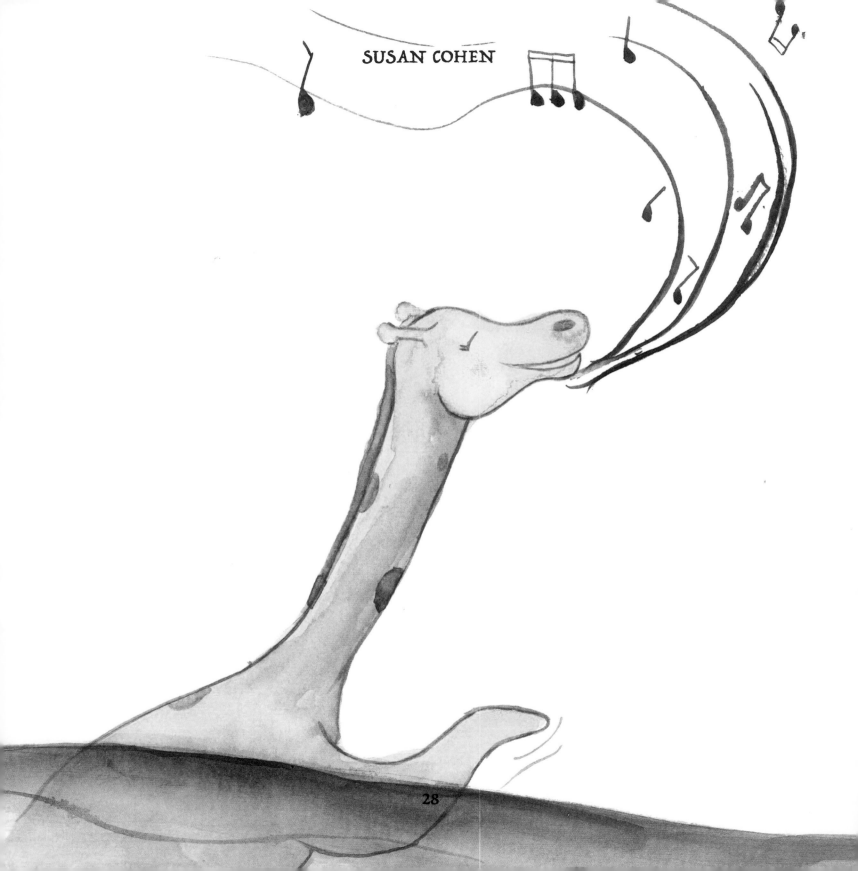

SUSAN COHEN

28

Life's a thousand songs
Life's a thousand dances
Full of great adventures
And endless chances

To be wonderful you
In all of your glory
To live happy, live free
And write your own story

So explore who you are
Be all you can be
Find your own flow
Be your own mystery!

31

SUSAN COHEN

First edition, 2021

The Wee Book Company Ltd

Copyright © Susan Cohen, The Wee Book Company Ltd

A catalogue record of this book is available
from the British Library. ISBN 9781913237370

Stay in touch with us as we send smiles all round the world.
Sign up for our newsletter at www.theweebookcompany.com

Printed in Great Britain by Bell and Bain Ltd, Glasgow